the bus

PAUL KIRCHNER

Futura

A Futura Book

First published in Great Britain in 1987 by
Futura Publications, a Division of Macdonald & Co (Publishers) Ltd
London & Sydney

The Bus first appeared in serial form in *Heavy Metal* magazine

ISBN 0 7088 8244 7

Printed and bound in Great Britain by
The Guernsey Press Co. Ltd, Guernsey, Channel Islands

Futura Publications
A Division of
Macdonald & Co (Publishers) Ltd
Greater London House
Hampstead Road
London NW1 7QX

A BPCC plc Company

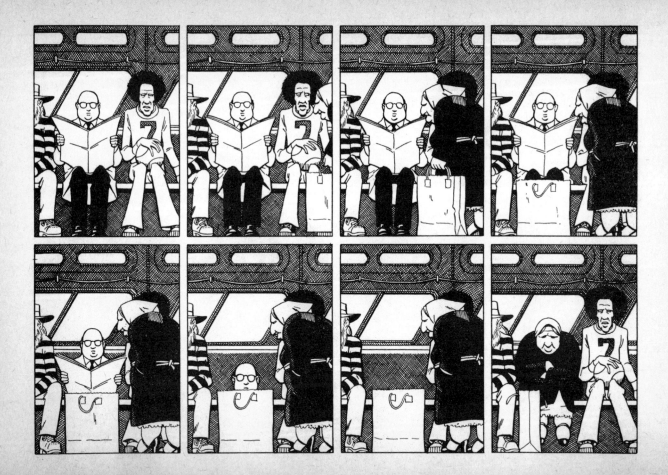

PRIMITIVE SEA-DWELLING ANCESTORS OF THE BUS APPEARED AS FAR BACK AS 500,000,000 B.C.

BY THE END OF THE MESOZOIC ERA, THE BUS AS WE KNOW IT HAD EVOLVED.

LA BREA

IN THE PLIOCENE ERA, VAST HERDS OF BUSES COVERED THE WORLD'S GRASSLANDS.

BUSES WERE HUNTED BY EARLY MAN, WHO STRIPPED THE CARCASSES OF VALUABLE PARTS AND ACCESSORIES. (FOR CENTURIES, BUSES WERE THE ONLY KNOWN SOURCE OF VULCANIZED RUBBER.)

THE ANCIENT EGYPTIANS WERE THE FIRST TO HARNESS THE POWER OF THE BUS, AND MADE EXTENSIVE USE OF THEM WHILE BUILDING THE PYRAMIDS.

THE EARLIEST KNOWN USE OF THE BUS IN ITS MASS TRANSIT ROLE WAS BY GENERAL HANNIBAL, WHO USED THEM TO TRANSPORT HIS ARMY ACROSS THE ALPS.

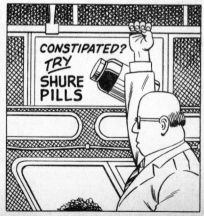

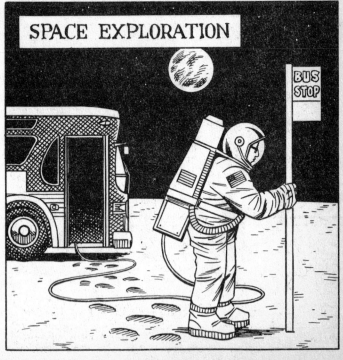

MASS TRANSIT

THE ARTS

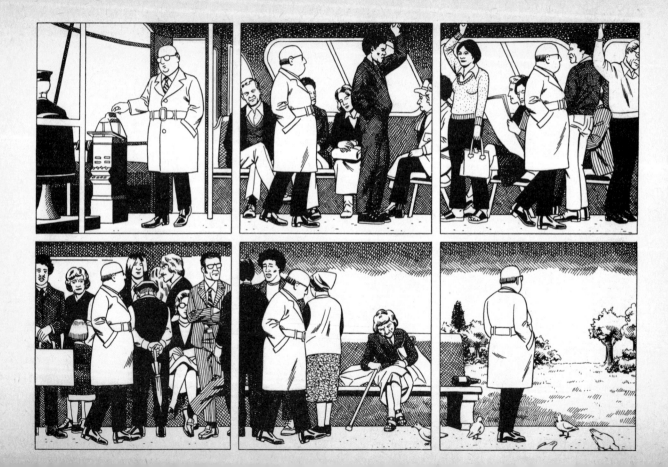

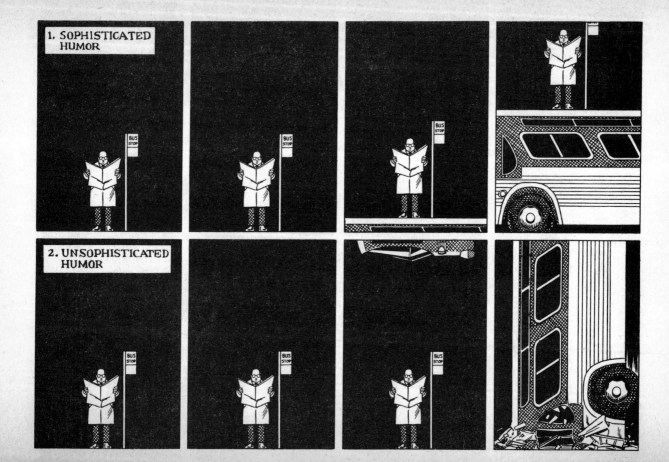

SHE WAS THE LARGEST OF HER KIND EVER BUILT...HER MAIDEN JOURNEY WAS THE SOCIAL EVENT OF THE YEAR.

SHE LEFT HER TERMINAL ON A CLEAR APRIL MORNING BOUND FOR THE EAST SIDE.

PASSENGERS IN FIRST CLASS WERE AFFORDED EVERY LUXURY...

WHILE CONDITIONS IN STEERAGE WERE DEPLORABLE.

THE DRIVER HAD BEEN WARNED OF POTHOLES EN ROUTE, BUT STUBBORNLY REFUSED TO REDUCE SPEED.

THE TERRIBLE TRAGEDY THAT RESULTED IS KNOWN TO ALL.

THE COMMUTERIST MANIFESTO

BY KARL BARX

IN ORDER TO JOIN THE WORLD REVOLUTIONARY STRUGGLE, WE MUST FIRST UNDERSTAND THE CLASS SYSTEM ...

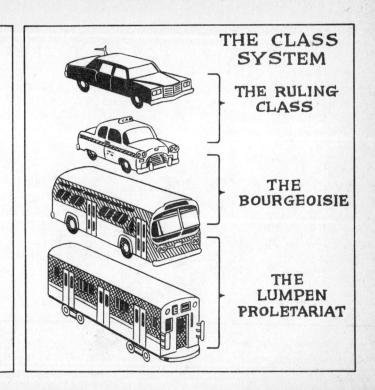

THE CLASS SYSTEM

THE RULING CLASS

THE BOURGEOISIE

THE LUMPEN PROLETARIAT

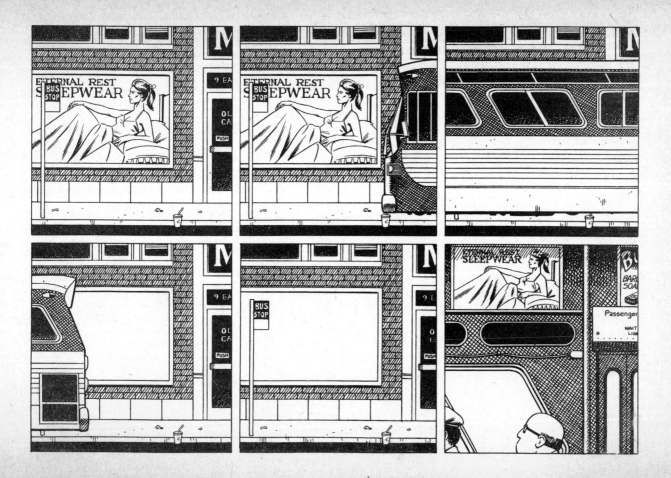

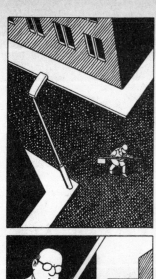

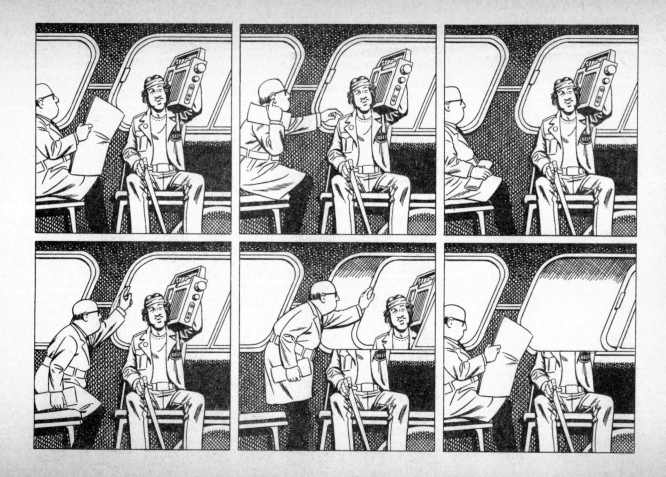

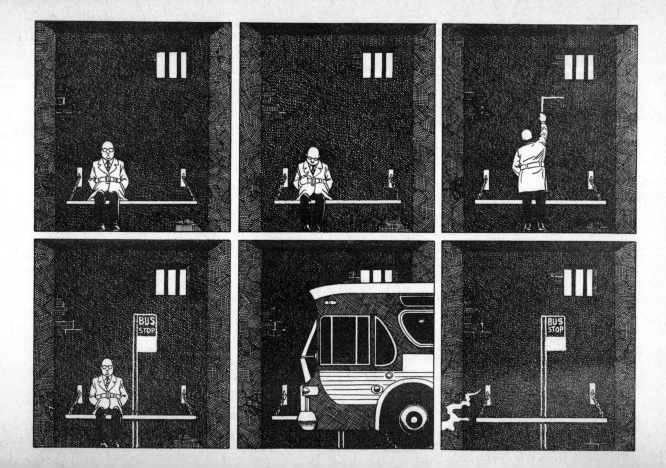

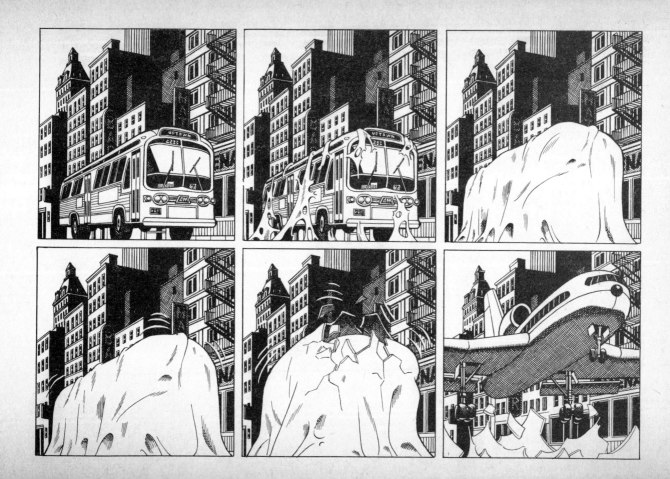

LATELY, IT SEEMS YOU CAN HARDLY PICK UP A MAGAZINE WITHOUT FINDING ONE FEATURED PROMINENTLY... YOU CAN BARELY TUNE INTO A T.V. TALK SHOW BEFORE THE DISCUSSION TURNS TO THEM... *AND SO WE ASK--*

WHAT IS IT WITH THE BUS?

CONSIDER...

FOR THE FIRST TIME SINCE 1957 *BUS DRIVER* IS THE LEADING VOCATIONAL CHOICE OF HIGH SCHOOL SENIORS SURVEYED...

TIME MAGAZINE BROKE TRADITION BY CHOOSING A MUNICIPAL BUS FROM AMES, IOWA, FOR ITS YEARLY "MAN OF THE YEAR" ISSUE...

TIME

DECEMBER 21, 1986 $1.50

MAN OF THE YEAR

IN SERVICE

MILLIONAIRE *MALCOLM FORBES* SWAPPED HIS CHAUFFEUR-DRIVEN STRETCH LIMO FOR A ROOMIER "BUS-FOR-ONE"...

YET LET US NOT FORGET THAT THERE ARE MANY AMONGST US, ESPECIALLY IN RURAL AREAS, WHO HAVE ONLY THE MOST RUDIMENTARY NOTION OF WHAT A BUS ACTUALLY *IS*. FOR THEM, THE FOLLOWING INTRODUCTION.

VITAL STATISTICS... *

FRONT

SIDE

BACK

ITS FUNCTION...

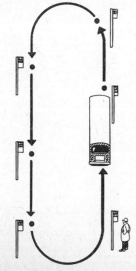

THE BUS FOLLOWS A SET ROUTE, STOPPING FREQUENTLY AT DESIGNATED POINTS.

*REMEMBER THAT THESE FIGURES ARE BASED ON STATISTICAL NORMS. INDIVIDUAL VARIATIONS MAY BE CONSIDERABLE. FOR EXAMPLE, DEPENDING ON AGE AND BUILD, A BUS MAY WEIGH ANYWHERE FROM SEVERAL HUNDRED TO 40,000 POUNDS!

PROCREATION AND UPBRINGING...

COURTSHIP

MATING

PREGNANCY

BIRTH

NURTURING

EDUCATION

NEW CONCEPTS IN THE BUS ARE KEEPING THIS AGE-OLD FRIEND OF MAN IN STEP WITH THE TIMES!

IN **NEW YORK**, BUSES ARE GOING **CONDO**--AS A PART OWNER OF A BUS, YOU PAY ONLY A MAINTENANCE FEE OF PERHAPS $3 A RIDE-- AND YOU CAN RENT OUT YOUR SEAT WHEN YOU'RE NOT USING IT!

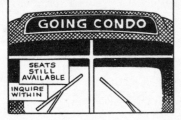

GOING CONDO

SEATS STILL AVAILABLE

INQUIRE WITHIN

BOSTON, MASS... RATHER THAN TIE UP CITY FUNDS IN LITTLE-USED EMERGENCY EQUIPMENT, BUSES DOUBLE AS **FIRE ENGINES**, WITH COMMUTERS BRIEFED IN THE BASICS OF FIREFIGHTING SHOULD THE NEED ARISE!

GANGWAY!

IN **DAYTON, OHIO**, BUS TRAVEL IS **FREE!** THE SYSTEM TURNS A PROFIT BY LEASING AISLE SEATS TO REAL ESTATE PROMOTERS, INSURANCE SALESMEN, AND SPOKESMEN FOR THE UNIFICATION CHURCH!

DALLAS, TEXAS HAS INTRODUCED A NEW CONCEPT IN BUS SHELTERS-- A **V.I.P. LOUNGE** FEATURING VIDEO GAMES, NAUTILUS EQUIPMENT, EVEN A SUSHI BAR!

Dinky Kong

IT HAS NOT BEEN THE PURPOSE OF THIS ARTICLE TO MAKE VALUE JUDGEMENTS ON THE COMPLEX AND CONTROVERSIAL ISSUES RAISED HEREIN. TO ITS SUPPORTERS, THE BUS REPRESENTS ALL THAT IS GOOD IN THE AMERICAN SPIRIT...TO ITS CRITICS, IT EPITOMIZES THE WORST ASPECTS OF CONTEMPORARY LIFE. SUFFICE IT TO SAY THAT, LIKE IT OR NOT, **BUSES ARE HERE TO STAY!**

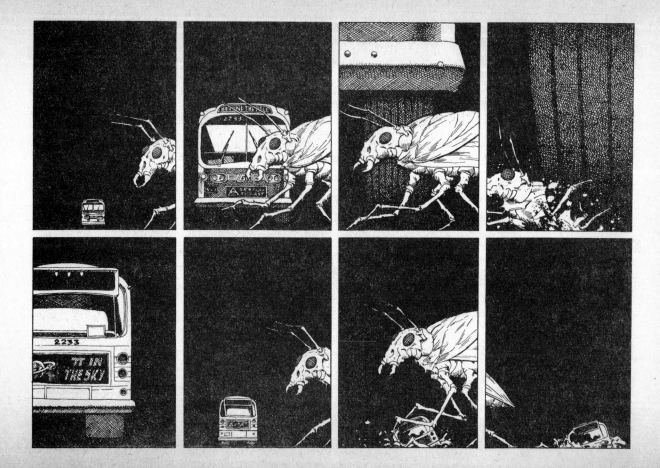

THE BIG QUESTIONS

FREE WILL *OR* PREDESTINATION?

SPIRITUAL QUEST *OR* SELF-DELUSION?

INDIVIDUAL RIGHTS *OR* SOCIETAL NEEDS?

INEVITABLE CONFLICT *OR* EVENTUAL COOPERATION?

CROSSTOWN AT 34th ST. *OR* UPTOWN TO 168th?

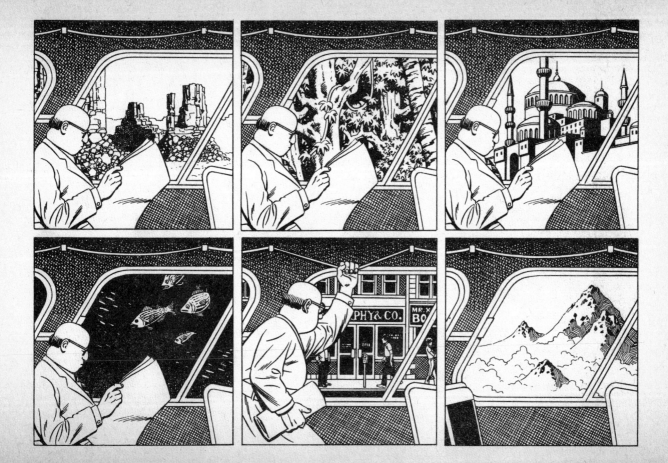

WORKING GIRL

CAN AN UPTOWN BUS FIND HAPPINESS ON THE STREETS OF THE BIG CITY? ARE YOU KIDDING? THIS MONTH'S BUS IS BUSY, BUSY, BUSY, BUT IN SPITE OF HER TIGHT SCHEDULE, SHE STILL FINDS TIME FOR FUN!

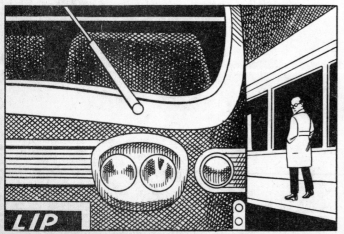

"I PICK MEN UP RIGHT OFF THE STREET SOMETIMES... I LIKE A MAN WHO CAN PAY HIS OWN WAY... WHO KNOWS WHERE HE'S GOING... LOOKS AREN'T IMPORTANT."

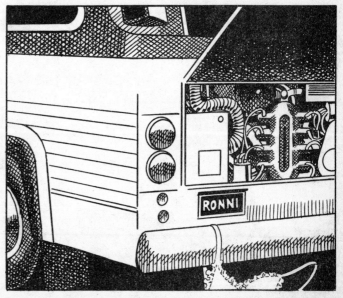

TURN ONS: Exact change, Green lights

TURN OFFS: Gridlock, Graffiti, Potholes

"I'M VERY SERIOUS ABOUT MY ACTING. I APPEARED IN *SPLASH*; OF COURSE IT WAS ONLY A DRIVE-ON PART, BUT IT WAS A VALUABLE LEARNING EXPERIENCE TO WORK WITH DIRECTOR RON HOWARD."

MISS MARCH

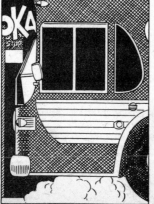

HE STARTED OUT LIKE ANY OTHER: NEAT, PUNCTUAL, EAGER TO SERVE.

GRADUALLY HIS BEHAVIOR CHANGED. IT STARTED WITH SMALL INFRACTIONS -- INOPERATIVE AIR-CONDITIONING, AN ILLEGIBLE SIGN...

COMMUTERS WERE IGNORED OR RUDELY SPLASHED WITH MUD.

SOON HE WAS SPORTING GRAFFITI AND TRAVELING IN A BAD PACK...

ONE NIGHT HE WENT TOO FAR. HE HELD PASSENGERS HOSTAGE, DEMANDING PAYMENT OF AN EXTRA FARE.

NOW HE SERVES TIME, LOCKED BEHIND A STEEL FENCE. WILL HE LEARN HIS LESSON, OR WILL HE EMERGE UNREPENTANT, MORE DANGEROUS THAN EVER?

IT'S UP TO HIM!

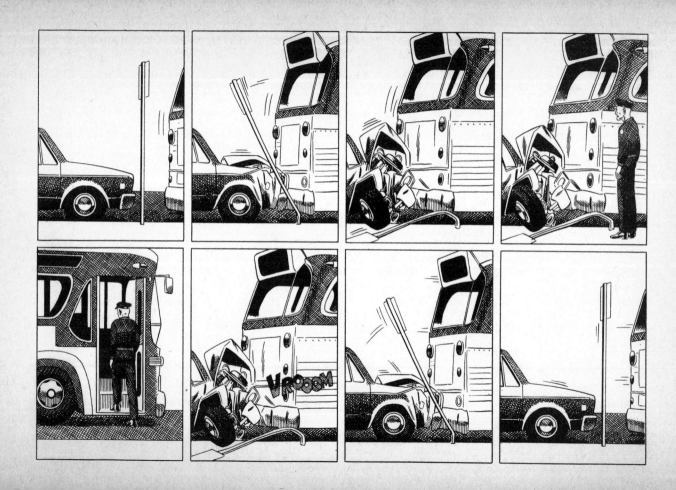

DO NOT OPEN WINDOW.
BUS IS SURROUNDED
BY HUGE MAN-EATING
SPIDER CRABS.

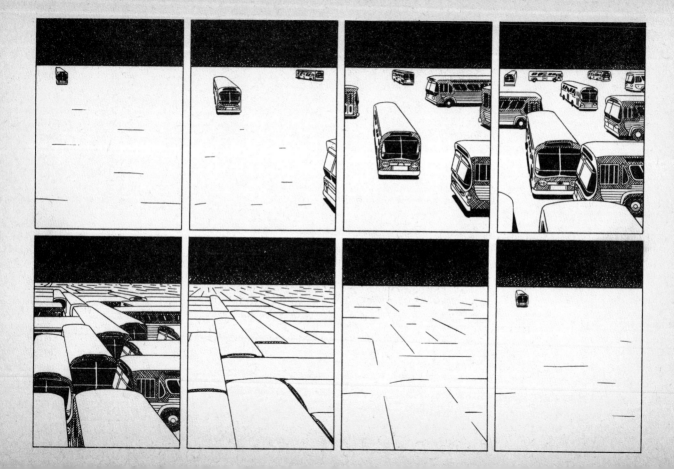

BELIEFS REGARDING DEATH AND THE AFTERLIFE

THE JAWS OF DEATH

FINAL JOURNEY

HALLOWED REST

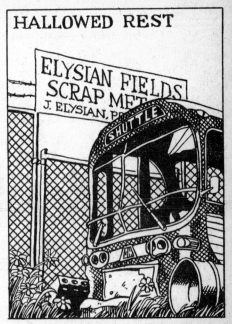

FORGING OF THE SPIRIT

RETURN TO THE PHYSICAL PLANE

REINCARNATION AT A HIGHER LEVEL

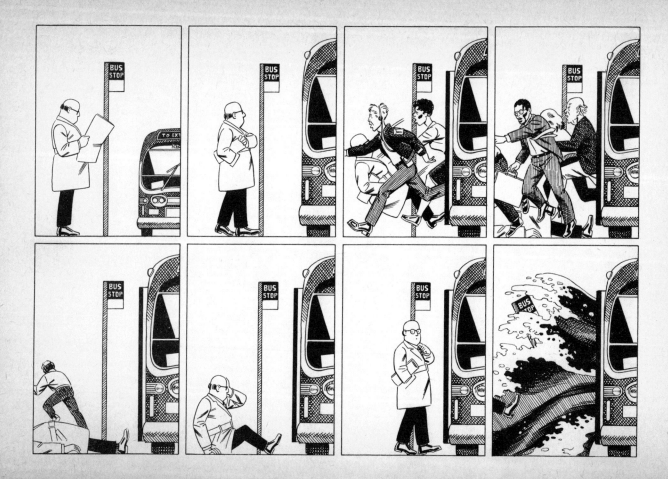

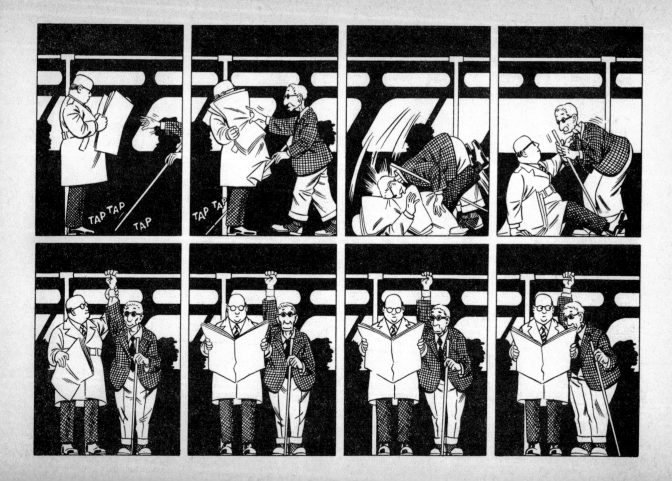

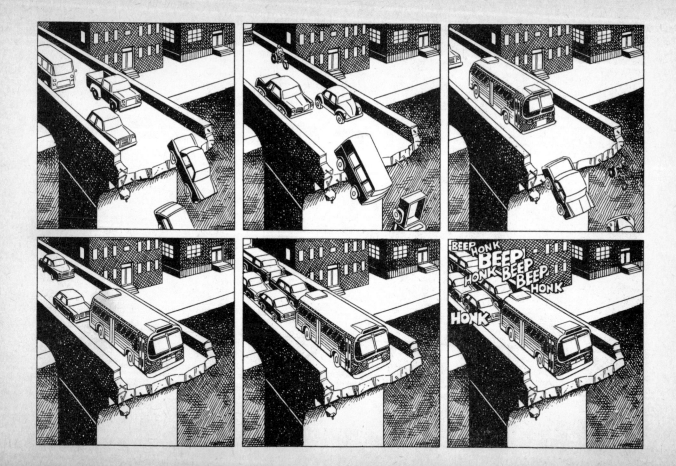

THE T-SHIRT:

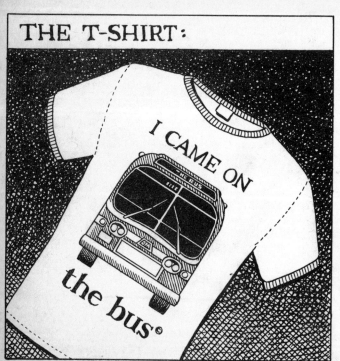

THE CALENDAR:

THE PLANTER:

THE COFFEE MUG:

l'expresso

THE "BUS-ON-A-ROPE":

THE RECORD: